The route to your roots

When they look back at their formative years, many Indians nostc
vital part Amar Chitra Katha picture books have played in their lives. It was **ACK** –
Amar Chitra Katha – that first gave them a glimpse of their glorious heritage.

Since they were introduced in 1967, there are now **over 400 Amar Chitra Katha**
titles to choose from. **Over 100 million copies** have been sold worldwide.

Now the Amar Chitra Katha titles are even more widely available in **1000+
bookstores all across India**. You can also buy all the titles through our online store
www.amarchitrakatha.com. We provide quick delivery anywhere in the world.

To make it easy for you to locate the titles of your choice from our treasure trove of
titles, the books are now arranged in five categories.

Epics and Mythology
Best known stories from the Epics and the Puranas

Indian Classics
Enchanting tales from Indian literature

Fables and Humour
Evergreen folktales, legends and tales of wisdom and humour

Bravehearts
Stirring tales of brave men and women of India

Visionaries
Inspiring tales of thinkers, social reformers and nation builders

Contemporary Classics
The Best of Modern Indian literature

Amar Chitra Katha Pvt Ltd
© Amar Chitra Katha Pvt Ltd, 1972, Reprinted September 2021,
ISBN 978-81-8482-217-5
Published by Amar Chitra Katha Pvt. Ltd., 204, 2nd Floor, Dhantak Plaza,
Makwana Road, Gamdevi, Marol, Andheri East, Mumbai 400059, India.
For Consumer Complaints Contact Tel : +91-22 49188881/2
Email: customerservice@ack-media.com
Printed in India By True Colour Print

The route to your roots

PRITHVIRAJ CHAUHAN

Jaichand was furious! His daughter Samyogita had eloped with Prithviraj Chauhan, the warrior king of Delhi. She, like many others, was smitten by tales of his daring, his nobility and his sense of honour. Though the young couple's happiness was doomed, even in his dying hour, it was the brave Prithviraj who chose how his life should end.

Script
Yagya Sharma

Illustrations
P.B.Kavadi

Editor
Anant Pai

Cover illustration by: C.M.Vitankar

PRITHVIRAJ CHAUHAN

MUCH BEFORE THE ADVENT OF THE MUGHALS IN INDIA, DELHI WAS RULED BY A BRAVE KING, PRITHVIRAJ CHAUHAN.

DURING THE SAME PERIOD, KANNAUJ, A MUCH BIGGER AND MORE POWERFUL KINGDOM THAN DELHI, WAS RULED BY JAICHAND.

MAHARAJ, YOU HAVE ONLY TO PERFORM THE RAJASUYA YAGNA TO BECOME AN EMPEROR.

I WISH I WERE THE EMPEROR OF INDIA.

A GOOD IDEA. THOSE WHO DARE OPPOSE ME SHALL BE DESTROYED.

INFORM ALL THE KINGS THAT THEY SHOULD ACCEPT ME AS THEIR MASTER AND PARTICIPATE IN MY RAJASUYA YAGNA.

AS YOU WISH, MAHARAJ!

THE KINGS WHO REFUSED TO ACCEPT JAICHAND AS THEIR RULER HAD TO FACE THE MIGHT OF HIS FORCES.

FINALLY, JAICHAND WAS ACCEPTED AS THE SOLE RULER BY ALL THE KINGS EXCEPT ONE.

I AM GLAD THAT ALL THESE KINGS ACCEPT MY SUPREMACY... BUT WHAT ABOUT PRITHVIRAJ?

THE MESSENGER HAS NOT YET RETURNED, MAHARAJ.

PRITHVIRAJ BECAME VERY ANGRY WITH JAICHAND'S MESSENGER. HIS GURU SPOKE TO THE MESSENGER.

GO AND TELL YOUR MASTER THAT DELHI WILL HAVE ONLY PRITHVIRAJ AS ITS KING.

PRITHVIRAJ WAS SO UPSET BY WHAT HE HAD HEARD THAT TO DROWN HIS ANGER, HE WENT ON A HUNTING EXPEDITION.

MEANWHILE, JAICHAND'S MESSENGER HAD REACHED KANNAUJ.

MAHARAJ! PRITHVIRAJ HAS REFUSED TO ACCEPT YOUR SUPREMACY.

I SHALL ATTACK DELHI AND PUNISH HIM.

BUT MAHARAJ, THE DATE OF THE YAGNA IS VERY NEAR. WE DON'T HAVE ENOUGH TIME TO ATTACK DELHI.

YOU ARE RIGHT. I'LL WAIT TILL THE YAGNA IS OVER. ALONG WITH THE YAGNA I SHALL HOLD MY DAUGHTER SAMYOGI-TA'S SWAYAMVAR.

AT THE SWAYAMVAR, SAMYOGITA SHALL CHOOSE HER HUSBAND FROM AMONGST THE INVITED KINGS.

AND I HAVE AN EXCELLENT PLAN TO HUMILIATE PRITHVIRAJ AT THE SWAYAMVAR.

BUT HAVING LISTENED TO MANY TALES OF PRITHVIRAJ'S BRAVERY, SAMYOGITA HAD FALLEN IN LOVE WITH HIM WITHOUT EVEN MEETING HIM.

THE SWAYAMVAR SHALL NOT TAKE PLACE.

BUT YOUR FATHER HAS ALREADY INVITED MANY KINGS.

I WILL NOT CHOOSE ANY OF THEM. I HAVE ALREADY CHOSEN MAHARAJ PRITHVIRAJ.

BUT YOUR FATHER DOESN'T LIKE HIM.

WHY? BECAUSE HE HAD THE COURAGE TO OPPOSE MY FATHER. I'LL MARRY PRITHVIRAJ AND NONE OTHER.

THE NEWS OF BOTH, THE HUMILIATION PLANNED FOR HIM BY JAICHAND, AND SAMYOGITA'S LOVE FOR HIM REACHED PRITHVIRAJ.

CHAND, MY FRIEND, MY HONOUR IS AT STAKE. I MUST MARRY SAMYOGITA.

BUT HOW WILL YOU DO THAT, MAHARAJ?

JAICHAND WILL NOT LET ME ENTER KANNAUJ. BUT HE WILL NOT STOP A LEARNED MAN LIKE YOU.

SO CHAND PROCEEDED TO KANNAUJ WITH PRITHVIRAJ DISGUISED AS HIS BETEL-CARRIER AND A HUNDRED SELECTED WARRIORS ALSO DISGUISED AS SERVANTS.

AFTER SEVERAL DAYS, THEY REACHED KANNAUJ.

THAT SHINING GOLD-COVERED DOME IS JAICHAND'S PALACE, MAHARAJ!

DON'T CALL ME MAHARAJ - I AM SUPPOSED TO BE YOUR SERVANT.

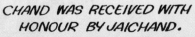

CHAND WAS RECEIVED WITH HONOUR BY JAICHAND.

I HAVE HEARD THAT PRITHVIRAJ IS A GOOD FIGHTER.

YES, HE CAN STRIKE FIFTY TIMES BEFORE HIS ENEMY EVEN RAISES HIS SWORD.

JAICHAND DID NOT LIKE CHAND'S REPLY BUT HE KEPT QUIET.

GO AND MAKE ARRANGEMENTS FOR OUR GUEST'S STAY.

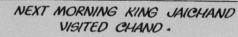

THEN JAICHAND RETIRED TO HIS PALACE.

NEXT MORNING KING JAICHAND VISITED CHAND.

I HOPE YOU ARE COMFORTABLE HERE.

WE ARE. PLEASE SIT DOWN.

JAICHAND WAS IMPRESSED BY THE PERSONALITY OF THE BETEL-CARRIER.

THIS MAN IS NOT AN ORDINARY SERVANT.

THERE IS SOMETHING STRANGE ABOUT THIS SERVANT.

WHILE GOING OUT, JAICHAND GLANCED THROUGH A WINDOW.

HE DOES NOT SEEM TO BE A SERVANT.

IMMEDIATELY JAICHAND ALERTED HIS FORCES.

GUARD ALL THE ROADS. KEEP AN EYE ON THOSE PEOPLE.

MEANWHILE, PRITHVIRAJ WAS PLANNING TO MEET SAMYOGITA.

WE CAN'T REMAIN SAFE HERE FOR LONG, SOMETHING MUST BE DONE SOON.

JAICHAND KNEW THAT HIS DAUGHTER HAD DECIDED TO MARRY PRITHVIRAJ AT ANY COST. HE QUICKLY CHANGED HIS PLANS.

MINISTER, INFORM ALL THE INVITED KINGS THAT THE SWAYAMWAR WILL TAKE PLACE TOMORROW, AND NOT WITH THE YAGNA, AS PLANNED EARLIER.

AS YOU WISH MAHARAJ.

AN EXCITED SOLDIER HURRIED TO PRITHVIRAJ.

MAHARAJ, WE HAVE NO TIME TO LOSE. THE SWAYAMWAR IS GOING TO TAKE PLACE TOMORROW.

SO SOON?

YES, AND JAICHAND IS GOING TO PLACE YOUR STATUE AT THE GATE TO HUMILIATE YOU.

HE SHALL PAY DEARLY FOR HUMILIAT- ING ME THUS.

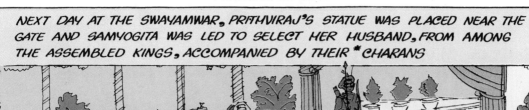

NEXT DAY AT THE SWAYAMWAR, PRITHVIRAJ'S STATUE WAS PLACED NEAR THE GATE AND SAMYOGITA WAS LED TO SELECT HER HUSBAND, FROM AMONG THE ASSEMBLED KINGS, ACCOMPANIED BY THEIR *CHARANS

I EXPECTED HIM TO BE PRESENT HERE IN DISGUISE...

WHAT SHALL I DO NOW...

FINALLY SAMYOGITA PUT THE GARLAND AROUND THE NECK OF PRITHVIRAJ'S STATUE.

MY HUSBAND CAN ONLY BE PRITHVIRAJ.

*CHARANS- POET WHO ACCOMPANIED KINGS TO SWAYAMWARS TO SING THEIR PRAISES WHEN THE PRINCES APPROACHED.

STOP THEM!

AND SAMYOGITA RODE WITH PRITHVIRAJ ON HIS HORSE.

COME MY SOLDIERS, LET US FIGHT OUR WAY OUT.

BUT WITHIN NO TIME JAICHAND'S HUGE ARMY HAD SURROUNDED THEM.

ATTACK AND CAPTURE PRITHVIRAJ AT ANY COST.

THE FIRST ATTACK ON PRITHVIRAJ WAS LED BY MIR BANDAN — A PERSIAN OFFICER IN JAICHAND'S ARMY.

BUT MIR BANDAN WAS NO MATCH FOR PRITHVIRAJ.

WITH MIR BANDAN'S DEATH, HIS SOLDIERS RAN HELTER-SKELTER.

THEN PRITHVIRAJ AND HIS SOLDIERS ATTACKED JAICHAND'S MAIN FORCES.

SOON PRITHVIRAJ WITH HIS SOLDIERS CRASHED THROUGH THE ENEMY LINES. THE SOLDIERS WERE JUBILANT.

BUT THEIR JOY WAS SHORT LIVED. CUNNING JAICHAND HAD PLACED MORE SOLDIERS FARTHER DOWN THE ROUTE.

THIS TIME PRITHVIRAJ WAS SERIOUSLY INJURED. BUT HE PULLED THE ARROW OUT.

THOUGH THEY PROVIDED SAFETY, THE HILLS CHECKED THE SPEED OF PRITHVIRAJ'S SOLDIERS. SO, THE ENEMY STARTED COMING CLOSER. ON A NARROW HILLY PATH —

WE WILL LEAVE ONE WARRIOR HERE TO ENGAGE THE ENEMY AND THE OTHERS WILL PROCEED TO DELHI.

NO..

...I AM NOT A COWARD, I WILL STAY HERE AND FACE THE ENEMY.

NOBODY CAN DOUBT YOUR BRAVERY, MAHARAJ. BUT OUR AIM IS NOT TO FIGHT THE ENEMY BUT TO AVENGE YOUR INSULT....

....AND THAT PURPOSE WILL NOT BE ACHIEVED IF YOU DO NOT REACH DELHI WITH YOUR BRIDE.

AFTER QUITE SOME PERSUASION, PRITHVIRAJ AGREED AND THEY LEFT BAGH RAI BEHIND TO CHECK THE ENEMY.

BAGH RAI WAS A FIERCE FIGHTER.

BUT HE WAS GREATLY OUTNUMBERED.

AFTER THE DEATH OF BAGH RAI, THE JUBILANT FORCES OF THE ENEMY RUSHED FORWARD.

BEWARE! THERE IS ANOTHER BLOCKING THE PATH.

MANY WERE THE LIVES, SACRIFICED FOR PRITHVIRAJ.

KANH, THE COMMANDER OF PRITHVIRAJ'S ARMY, DECIDED TO CHECK THE ENEMY HIMSELF.

EVEN KANH'S HORSE ATTACKED THE ENEMY.

AFTER A BITTER FIGHT—

THERE! HE TOO IS KILLED.

NOW WE CAN CAPTURE PRITHVIRAJ WITH EASE.

BUT BY THEN, IT WAS TOO LATE. PRITHVIRAJ HAD REACHED HIS FORT IN DELHI.

AFRAID TO FIGHT PRITHVIRAJ'S VAST ARMY, THE FRUSTRATED JAICHAND WENT BACK.

THERE WAS GREAT REJOICING IN DELHI.

LONG LIVE MAHARAJ PRITHVIRAJ. LONG LIVE MAHARANI SAMYOGITA.

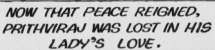

NOW THAT PEACE REIGNED, PRITHVIRAJ WAS LOST IN HIS LADY'S LOVE.

WE HAVE NOT SEEN OUR KING FOR A LONG TIME.

HE DOESN'T EVEN COME OUT OF HIS PALACE.

EVERYONE IS UNHAPPY.

YES, OUR KING HAS NOT COME TO THE COURT SINCE HE GOT MARRIED.

PRITHVIRAJ'S GURU WAS ALSO UNHAPPY.

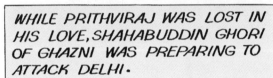

IT IS A PITY THAT A BRAVE, FEARLESS NOBLE WARRIOR LIKE PRITHVIRAJ SHOULD CARE SO MUCH FOR A WOMAN AND FORGET HIS DUTIES.

BUT SAMYOGITA IS NOT AN ORDINARY WOMAN.

NOR ARE THE PROBLEMS OF THE STATE ORDINARY.

WHILE PRITHVIRAJ WAS LOST IN HIS LOVE, SHAHABUDDIN GHORI OF GHAZNI WAS PREPARING TO ATTACK DELHI.

ALL THE SEVEN TIMES PRITHVIRAJ HAD DEFEATED, CAPTURED AND VERY GEN-EROUSLY RELEASED GHORI TO SEND HIM BACK HOME.

THIS TIME GHORI WAS CONFIDENT OF VICTORY AS JAICHAND HAD PROMISED TO HELP HIM IF NECESSARY.

JAICHAND IS MY ALLY. THIS IS MY CHANCE TO DEFEAT PRITHVIRAJ.

AND THUS WITH THE HELP OF THE TREACHEROUS JAICHAND SHAHABUDDIN THIS TIME RAISED A MUCH LARGER FORCE.

THE NOBLES OF DELHI WERE WORRIED BY THE ADVANCE OF SHAHABUDDIN'S FORCES.

BUT HOW CAN WE INFORM THE KING? HE GETS ANGRY WHEN DISTURBED.

I WILL WRITE HIM A LETTER.

A LETTER FROM MY GURU... WHY?

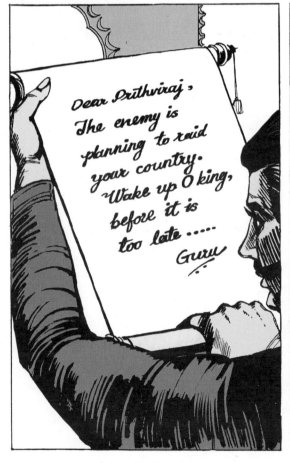

Dear Prithviraj,
The enemy is planning to raid your country. Wake up O king, before it is too late.....
Guru

SHAME ON ME! I NEGLECTED MY DUTIES AS A KING.

24

PRITHVIRAJ'S FORCES HAD GROWN WEAK AS HE HAD LOST THE COMMANDER AND THE CREAM OF HIS WARRIORS IN THE BATTLE WITH JAICHAND. BUT HE GATHERED THE REMAINING SOLDIERS AND LED THEM TO FACE THE ENEMY.

SHAHABUDDIN GHORI'S FORCES WERE LED BY THREE VETERAN OFFICERS.

SOON THE TWO ARMIES WERE FIGHTING EACH OTHER.

PRITHVIRAJ AND HIS SOLDIERS FOUGHT WITH EXCEPTIONAL BRAVERY.

BUT PRITHVIRAJ'S SMALL FORCE WAS MASSACRED AND HE WAS CAPTURED BY GHORI'S SOLDIERS.

CAPTIVE PRITHVIRAJ WAS TAKEN TO GHAZNI.

LOOK AT THE FIERCE LION OF DELHI.

HA! HA

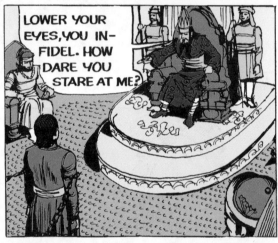

LOWER YOUR EYES, YOU IN-FIDEL. HOW DARE YOU STARE AT ME?

UNAFRAID, PRITHVIRAJ CONTINUED TO STARE.

GUARDS! DESTROY HIS EYES!

AND SO PRITHVIRAJ'S EYES WERE BURNT.

WHEN POET CHAND HEARD ABOUT PRITHVIRAJ'S FATE, HE DRESSED AS A SADHU AND STARTED AT ONCE FOR GHAZNI.

CHAND MET SHAHABUDDIN WHEN HE WAS PRACTISING ARCHERY.

WHAT DO YOU THINK OF MY AIM?

GOOD, BUT VERY ORDINARY COMPARED TO MAHARAJ PRITHVIRAJ'S SKILL....

....HE CAN PIERCE A METAL GONG WITH A HEADLESS ARROW.

IMPOSSIBLE.

IT IS NOT IMPOSSIBLE. ALTHOUGH HE IS BLIND HE CAN DO IT, GUIDED ONLY BY THE SOUND OF THE GONG.

I WANT TO SEE IT, BUT IF HE FAILS, YOUR HEAD WILL BE CUT OFF.

CHAND MET PRITHVIRAJ IN THE PRISON AND TOLD HIM OF HIS PLAN.

YOU CAN KILL SHAHABUDDIN DURING THE DEMONSTRATION AND AVENGE YOUR INSULT. AND THEN WE CAN STAB EACH OTHER.

BUT HOW WILL I KNOW WHERE HE IS SITTING.

LEAVE THAT TO ME.

ALL RIGHT.

MAHARAJ PRITHVIRAJ HAS TO GIVE A DEMONSTRATION. BUT SINCE HE IS A KING, HE WILL NOT OBEY A COMMON MAN'S ORDER. YOU WILL HAVE TO ORDER HIM TO SHOOT.

AGREED

AT THE COURT, NEXT DAY—

READY.....AIM

AT THE LAST ORDER, PRITHVIRAJ WHIRLED ROUND AND AIMED AT SHAHABUDDIN GUIDED BY HIS VOICE.

SHOOT.....aaa...ah

PRITHVIRAJ LEARNT FROM HIS KEEN SENSE OF HEARING THAT HIS ENEMY WAS DEAD.

TO AVOID A HUMILIATING DEATH AT THE HANDS OF ENEMY SOLDIERS CHAND AND PRITHVIRAJ STABBED EACH OTHER AS PREVIOUSLY PLANNED.

VICTORY TO MAHARAJ PRITHVIRAJ.

RANA KUMBHA

PILLAR OF RAJPUT PRIDE

The route to your roots

RANA KUMBHA

'Victory for Mewar!' His father's last words seemed to spur the young ruler on to ever greater feats. His success on the battlefield raised Rajput pride as high as the magnificent tower at Chittor, which he completed in 1448. Tirelessly subduing mighty sultans as well as sly traitors, Rana Kumbha ensured that his name was inscribed as one of the land's most worthy sons.

Script
Jagjit Uppal

Illustrations
H.S.Chavan &
Dilip Kadam

Editor
Anant Pai

Cover illustration by: Pratap Mulick

RANA KUMBHA

MAHARANA MOKAL, THE RULER OF MEWAR, WAS CAMPING AT BAGOR (NEAR CHITTOR) WHILE ON A TOUR OF HIS KINGDOM. ONE QUIET AFTERNOON THE RANA WAS RESTING IN HIS TENT.

NOT FAR AWAY, TWO OF HIS OFFICERS, THE BROTHERS CHACHA AND MERA, WERE CONSPIRING WITH ANOTHER OFFICER, MAHPA, TO MURDER HIM.

MAHPA, THE RANA HAS INSULTED US. SOME TIME AGO, IN THE PRESENCE OF ALL THE CHIEFS, HE POINTED TO A TREE AND ASKED ME WHAT IT WAS CALLED.

HE WANTED TO REMIND US THAT OUR GRANDFATHER WAS A CARPENTER.

HE SHALL PAY WITH HIS LIFE.

WE SHALL AVENGE THIS INSULT.

YOU HAVE MY SUPPORT.

1

LOOKING FOR FURTHER SUPPORT, THE THREE MEN ASKED MALESI, THE RANA'S CHIEF GUARD, TO JOIN THEM. BUT THE LOYAL GUARD INFORMED THE RANA OF THE CONSPIRACY.

... AND NOW CHACHA AND MERA HAVE WON THE SUPPORT OF MAHPA. WE MUST BE ON OUR GUARD.

THE RANA DID NOT TAKE THE WARNING SERIOUSLY.

CHACHA AND MERA? WE CAN TAKE CARE OF THEM WITH EASE! BUT I DON'T THINK THEY WILL DARE TO RISE AGAINST ME.

HE WAS WRONG. THE VERY NEXT DAY, THE CONSPIRATORS DECIDED TO STRIKE. AS THEY RODE TOWARDS THE RANA'S TENT IT WAS PRINCE KUMBHA WHO ALERTED THE RANA.

FATHER! CHACHA AND MERA ARE COMING WITH THEIR MEN.

QUICK! BRING MY WEAPONS.

EVEN AS RANA MOKAL AND THE OTHERS GOT READY...

...THE CONSPIRATORS ENTERED THE TENT.

TRAITORS! IS THIS HOW YOU REPAY YOUR BENEFACTOR!

YOU INSULT US IN PUBLIC AND THEN CALL YOURSELF OUR BENEFACTOR! CHARGE, MERA! GET TO WORK, MAHPA!

THE RANA DREW HIS SWORD AND ...

... HIS BLADE CLASHED WITH THOSE OF THE TRAITORS.

RANI HADI* BRAVELY ENTERED THE FRAY.

BUT THE RUTHLESS CONSPIRATORS SHOWED HER NO MERCY. WHEN SHE FELL, THE RANA CRIED OUT TO HIS YOUNG SON —

KUMBHA! FLEE! WASTE NO TIME!

I CAN'T LEAVE YOU, FATHER! I'LL FIGHT WITH YOU.

* KUMBHA'S STEP-MOTHER

AS MORE MEN ENTERED THE TENT —

KUMBHA, YOU MUST ESCAPE FOR THE SAKE OF MEWAR! RIGHT NOW!

I'LL OBEY MY FATHER, THOUGH I MUST LEAVE HIM TO FIGHT ALONE.

KUMBHA! I'M DYING....VICTORY TO MEWAR!

I WILL NOT REST UNTIL I HAVE AVENGED YOUR MURDER, FATHER!

INSIDE THE TENT —
THE RANA IS DEAD. BUT HIS SON STILL LIVES.

WE'LL GO AFTER HIM.

MEANWHILE, KUMBHA HAD FLED TO A PATEL'S HOUSE NEAR BY.

THE RANA HAS BEEN MURDERED. I NEED A HORSE TO TAKE ME TO CHITTOR.

THE PATEL QUICKLY TOOK HIM TO HIS STABLES.

THESE TWO HORSES ARE THE FASTEST IN MEWAR. THEY ARE YOURS.

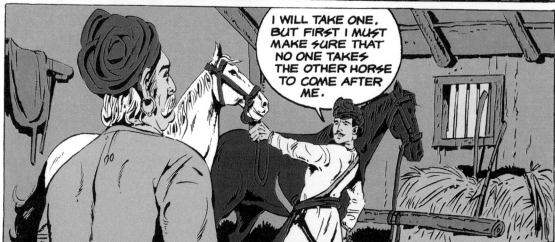

I WILL TAKE ONE, BUT FIRST I MUST MAKE SURE THAT NO ONE TAKES THE OTHER HORSE TO COME AFTER ME.

* VILLAGE CHIEF

MEANWHILE THE CONSPIRATORS WERE HOT ON THE TRAIL OF KUMBHA.

HE COULDN'T HAVE GONE FAR.

SUDDENLY—

LOOK! KUMBHA IS RIDING AWAY!

AFTER HIM!

WE'D BETTER GIVE UP. AT THAT SPEED WE WILL NEVER CATCH UP WITH HIM.

I RECOGNISE THAT HORSE. IT'S THE PATEL'S. BUT HE HAS ANOTHER HORSE THAT IS AS FAST.

LET'S GO AND GET IT.

THEY BURST INTO THE PATEL'S STABLE.

WE HAVE BEEN FORESTALLED! KUMBHA HAS KILLED THE SECOND HORSE.

COME, LET'S NOT WASTE ANY TIME. WE MUST CAPTURE KUMBHA BEFORE HE REACHES CHITTOR.

BUT KUMBHA HAD ALREADY REACHED CHITTOR.

CLOSE THE GATES! BE QUICK!

8

WE ARE TOO LATE ! KUMBHA HAS ESCAPED.

NEVER MIND. WE'LL GET HIM SOME OTHER TIME.

LATER, KUMBHA WAS CROWNED RANA OF CHITTOR.

AFTER THE CORONATION, KUMBHA CONFERRED WITH HIS GRANDMOTHER, HANSA BAI.

MAHPA, CHACHA AND MERA ARE STILL AT LARGE. I MUST PURSUE THEM.

NO, KUMBHA! DON'T LEAVE CHITTOR TILL YOU HAVE CONSOLIDATED YOUR POSITION. SEND WORD TO MY BROTHER WHO WILL CERTAINLY HELP YOU.

KUMBHA SENT AN ENVOY TO RAO RAN MAL, THE RATHOD KING OF MARWAR.

RANA MOKAL HAS BEEN MURDERED! I BOW MY HEAD IN SHAME FOR NOT PREVENTING THIS.

HE TOOK OFF HIS TURBAN AND THREW IT TO THE GROUND.

I VOW NOT TO WEAR A PUGRI TILL THIS FOUL DEED IS AVENGED.

THEREAFTER, HE BEGAN WEARING A PHENTA—A SIMPLE HEAD-DRESS.

RAO RAN MAL THEN WENT TO CHITTOR.

THE TREACHEROUS ASSAULT ON RANA MOKAL BURNS MY HEART...

...AND A VOLCANO ERUPTS IN EVERY FIBRE OF MY BEING.

RAO RAN MAL SET OUT TOWARDS THE PAI KOTRA HILLS WHERE THE TRAITORS WERE HIDING.

WHEN HE REACHED THE FOOT OF THE HILLS, HE ASKED THE BHILS, THE TRIBALS OF THE AREA, FOR INFORMATION ABOUT THE TRAITORS.

YOUR MAJESTY, IT IS TRUE THEY ARE HIDING IN THE FORT. BUT WAIT FOR A FEW DAYS. A LIONESS HAS JUST GIVEN BIRTH TO A CUB AND THE PATH IS BLOCKED.

I CAN'T WAIT. I MUST START CLIMBING THE HILL AT ONCE.

RAO RAN MAL BEGAN THE HAZARDOUS CLIMB WITH SIXTY TRUSTED MEN.

AS THE PARTY REACHED A LEDGE OF ROCK—

IT IS THE LIONESS!

RAN MAL'S SON JUMPED FORWARD...

... AND BEFORE THE LIONESS COULD ATTACK..

...HE BURIED HIS DAGGER INTO HER HEART.

THE PARTY SOON REACHED THE SUMMIT. RAO RAN MAL'S SOLDIERS SCRAMBLED OVER THE PARAPET.

JUST THEN, THE DRUMMER ACCOMPANYING RAO RAN MAL'S ARMY SLIPPED AND...

...HIS DRUM FELL DOWN...

... WITH A RE-SOUNDING CRASH.

INSIDE THE FORT, CHACHA'S DAUGHTER WOKE UP WITH A START.

FATHER! DID YOU HEAR THAT? PERHAPS KUMBHA'S MEN ARE HERE!

IT'S ONLY THE SOUND OF THUNDER! GO TO SLEEP, CHILD. KUMBHA'S MEN WON'T DARE TO CLIMB THIS STEEP HILL.

BUT SUDDENLY—

FATHER!

CHACHA WHIRLED ROUND.

RAO RAN MAL! *YOU!*

YES! I AM HERE TO AVENGE THE MURDER OF RANA MOKAL.

AARGH!

AFTER KILLING CHACHA AND MERA, RAO RAN MAL WENT IN SEARCH OF MAHPA.

HE'S NOT HERE. THE BIRD HAS FLOWN.

THANK GOD! THEY DON'T SUSPECT A THING.

MAHPA ESCAPED IN THE GUISE OF A WOMAN.

RAO RAN MAL RETURNED TO KUMBHA'S PALACE AT CHITTOR.

WE'VE TAKEN CARE OF CHACHA AND MERA. BUT MAHPA CANNOT BE FOUND.

A FEW YEARS LATER A MESSENGER CALLED ON KUMBHA.

YOUR MAJESTY, MAHPA HAS BEEN SEEN IN MANDU.

I'LL ASK SULTAN MAHMUD KHILJI TO RETURN THE CRIMINAL TO US.

SOME TIME LATER, KUMBHA'S ENVOY RETURNED AFTER MEETING THE SULTAN.

YOUR MAJESTY, THE SULTAN SAYS THAT MAHPA IS NOW UNDER HIS PROTECTION AND REFUSES TO SEND HIM BACK.

KUMBHA TURNED TO HIS UNCLE.

IF THE SULTAN WILL NOT SEND MAHPA TO CHITTOR WE WILL GO TO MANDU TO BRING HIM, WON'T WE, UNCLE?

SO RANA KUMBHA AND RAN MAL LEFT CHITTOR WITH THEIR FORCES.

THEY WERE INTERCEPTED NEAR SARANGPUR* BY THE SULTAN'S ARMY.

THE RAJPUTS PUT UP A VERY STRONG FIGHT AND THE SULTAN WAS FORCED TO RETREAT TO THE FORTRESS OF MANDU.

FALL BACK! BACK TO THE FORT!

* SITUATED BETWEEN CHITTOR AND MANDSAUR

THE RAJPUTS PURSUED THE RETREATING ARMY AND LAID SIEGE TO THE FORTRESS OF MANDU.

I WONDER HOW LONG THEY CAN HOLD OUT.

I THINK WE SHOULD ATTACK WITHOUT DELAY.

MEANWHILE, SULTAN MAHMUD KHILJI SENT FOR MAHPA.

MAHPA, I CAN NO LONGER GIVE YOU SHELTER. GO AND SEEK THE RANA'S PARDON.

THE RANA WILL SHOW ME NO MERCY. I'D BETTER ESCAPE.

HE RODE UP TO THE RAMPARTS OF THE FORT...

I ONLY HOPE I WILL NOT BE SPOTTED BY THE RAJPUTS.

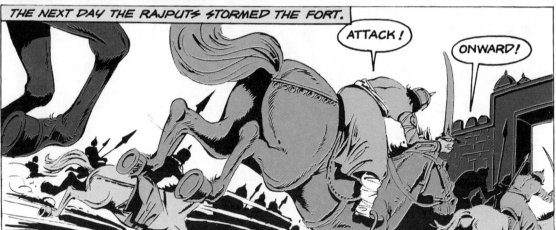

MAHMUD KHILJI WAS TAKEN CAPTIVE.

SULTAN, WHERE IS MAHPA?

YOU HAVEN'T FOUND HIM? SO I HAVE THE LAST LAUGH IT APPEARS. YOU HAVE ME, BUT NOT MAHPA!

WE WILL GET HIM YET, IF HE IS STILL ALIVE!*

RANA KUMBHA RETURNED TO CHITTOR IN TRIUMPH.

WE WILL BUILD A PILLAR TO COMMEMORATE OUR VICTORY OVER MAHMUD KHILJI.

SCULPTORS AND SKILLED ARTISANS CAME FROM FAR AND NEAR TO WORK ON THE PILLAR OF VICTORY.

IT'S OUR PRIVILEGE TO WORK FOR RANA KUMBHA.

HE HAS RESTORED THE GLORY OF THE RAJPUTS.

* YEARS LATER, MAHPA SOUGHT AND OBTAINED KUMBHA'S PARDON.

SIX MONTHS LATER —

SULTAN! I NOW RELEASE YOU AND ALSO RETURN MANDU TO YOU. GO, AND FROM NOW ON DO NOT GIVE ASYLUM TO MURDERERS!

YOU ARE GRACIOUS, RANA.

I WILL AVENGE THIS HUMILIATION.

THE RANA'S PREOCCUPATION DURING THE SIEGE OF MANDU HAD MADE A FEW OF HIS VASSALS BOLD.

YOUR MAJESTY, THE CHIEFS OF ABU AND BUNDI HAVE REBELLED.

WE WILL DEAL FIRMLY WITH THESE MEN.

RAN MAL WAS BY NOW DEAD. BUT KUMBHA WAS ABLE TO QUELL HIS REBELLIOUS VASSALS WITH EASE.

VICTORY TO KUMBHA!

IN 1444, KUMBHA WAS AT HARAVATI PUNISHING SOME REBELS, WHEN HE RECEIVED A MESSAGE FROM CHITTOR.

SULTAN KHILJI'S ARMY IS RANSACKING THE OUTSKIRTS OF MEWAR.

I WILL DEAL WITH THE SULTAN AT ONCE.

KUMBHA'S ARMY CAME UPON THE SULTAN'S FORCES NEAR MANDALGARH.

ATTACK!

SULTAN MAHMUD KHILJI WAS ONCE AGAIN DEFEATED BY THE RANA AND HAD TO FLEE.

MEANWHILE, WORK ON THE RANA'S VICTORY PILLAR CONTINUED. IT WAS COMPLETED IN 1448.

* THE FORT BUILT BY KUMBHA ON A HIGH PEAK OF THE WESTERN RANGE OF THE ARAVALI HILLS.

KUMBHA ADVANCED UPON NAGAUR AND STORMED THE FORT.

AS MUJAHID KHAN FLED FOR HIS LIFE . . .

. . . KUMBHA ENTERED THE FORT IN TRIUMPH WITH SHAMSKHAN BY HIS SIDE.

KUMBHA PLACED SHAMSKHAN ON THE THRONE.

I AM VERY GRATEFUL TO YOU, MAHARANA. BUT FOR YOUR HELP I WOULD NOT HAVE GOT BACK MY KINGDOM.

LATER SOME OF SHAMSKHAN'S COUNCILLORS CALLED ON HIM.

SULTAN, YOU SHOULD NOT DEMOLISH THE BATTLEMENTS. IT WOULD BE INSULTING TO YOU.

I WILL SEE WHAT I CAN DO TO PUT IT OFF.

SHAMSKHAN CALLED ON KUMBHA.

RANA, I HAVE NOT FORGOTTEN MY PROMISE TO DEMOLISH A PART OF THE BATTLEMENTS OF THE FORT. I REQUEST YOU TO GIVE ME A LITTLE MORE TIME.

ALL RIGHT. YOU MAY HAVE SOME MORE TIME.

AND KUMBHA RETURNED TO KUMBHAL-GARH. A FEW DAYS LATER —

RANA, SHAMSKHAN HAS NO INTENTION OF CARRYING OUT HIS PROMISE. INSTEAD OF DEMOLISHING THE BATTLE-MENTS, HE IS BUSY STRENGTHENING THEM.

HE HAS BETRAYED ME! I CAN'T ALLOW HIM TO GET AWAY WITH IT!

KUMBHA MARCHED TO NAGAUR AGAIN AND TOOK THE FORT AFTER DRIVING OUT SHAMSKHAN.

DEMOLISH THE FORTIFICATIONS!

SHAMSKHAN FLED TO AHMEDABAD AND SOUGHT THE HELP OF QUTB-UD-DIN, SULTAN OF GUJARAT.

SHAMSKHAN, I'LL DRIVE KUMBHA OUT OF NAGAUR.

WE MUST MAKE THOROUGH PREPARATIONS. KUMBHA IS NO ORDINARY MILITARY COMMANDER.

THE SULTAN OF GUJARAT SENT HIS SOLDIERS TO NAGAUR, BUT THEY WERE EASILY DEFEATED BY KUMBHA.

THE ENRAGED QUTB-UD-DIN SENT FOR HIS COMMANDER-IN-CHIEF, IMAD-UL-MULK.

I HAVE DECIDED TO TAKE KUMBHAL-GARH, BUT IT WON'T BE POSSIBLE IF KUMBHA IS THERE TO DEFEND IT. WE MUST DRAW HIM AWAY FROM KUMBHAL-GARH.

YOUR MAJESTY, I HAVE HEARD THAT KUMBHA IS CAMPING AT FORT ABU. I WILL LAY SIEGE TO ABU.

YES. DO THAT AND KEEP HIM BUSY WHILE I INVADE KUMBHALGARH.

WHEN THE SULTAN REACHED THE FOOT OF THE HILL ON WHICH THE FORTRESS OF KUMBHALGARH STOOD—

YOUR MAJESTY, AN ARMY IS ADVANCING FROM THE DIRECTION OF ABU.

WHAT! IS IT POSSIBLE THAT KUMBHA HAS DEFEATED IMAD-UL-MULK AND IS COMING BACK?

BUT SOON THE SULTAN'S FEARS WERE DISPELLED. IT WAS IMAD-UL-MULK'S ARMY THAT WAS APPROACHING.

YOUR MAJESTY, OUR ARMY WAS BATTERED BY KUMBHA. WE HAD TO RUN FOR OUR LIVES.

IT WAS INDEED KUMBHA. HE HAD REACHED KUMBHALGARH BY ANOTHER ROUTE AND HAD COME OUT TO COUNTER THE SULTAN'S ATTACK.

KUMBHA DEFEATED THE SULTAN OF GUJARAT WHO WAS FORCED TO RETRACE HIS STEPS. ON HIS WAY BACK—

SULTAN, I AM TEJ KHAN, THE PRIME MINISTER OF SULTAN KHILJI. IF THE FORCES OF MANDU AND GUJARAT JOIN HANDS, KUMBHA CAN BE EASILY DEFEATED.

I AM PREPARED TO ENTER INTO AN ALLIANCE WITH THE SULTAN OF MANDU.

AT CHITTOR—

RANA, THE GUJARAT FORCES ARE ADVANCING TOWARDS KUMBHALGARH. AND MAHMUD KHILJI IS PREPARING TO MARCH TOWARDS CHITTOR. THEY HAVE FORGED AN ALLIANCE AGAINST MEWAR.

PREPARE TO MEET THE GUJA-RAT FORCES FIRST. THE SUL-TAN OF MANDU, TOO, WILL GET A FITTING RECEPTION.

RANA KUMBHA'S FORCES MET THE ARMY OF GUJARAT AT MANDALGARH. IN THE BATTLE, THE RAJPUTS SUFFERED HEAVY LOSSES IN MEN AND EQUIPMENT.

MY MEN ARE FALLING. WE MUST RETREAT — AND NOW IS THE TIME TO DO SO.

IN PITCH DARKNESS, THEY RETREATED TO A HILLY CAVERN.

THAT NIGHT RANA KUMBHA SPOKE TO HIS MEN.

MY BRAVE MEN! IF WE LOSE THIS BATTLE, THE SULTAN OF MANDU WILL OCCUPY CHITTOR WHICH IS SACRED TO US.

NO! NEVER.

THEN TOMORROW MORNING WE WILL RESUME THE ATTACK WITH RENEWED STRENGTH. THE ENEMY WILL BE TAKEN UNAWARES. THEY THINK WE HAVE LOST HEART.

RANA, WE WILL ATTACK! JAI MEWAR! JAI EKA-LINGJI!

IN THE MORNING, THE RAJPUT ATTACK WAS SO FEROCIOUS...

...THAT THE GUJARAT FORCES WERE DEFEATED.

JAI EKALINGJI!

LONG LIVE RANA KUMBHA!

MEANWHILE, THE SULTAN OF MANDU HAD LAID SIEGE TO THE FORT OF CHITTOR.

SINCE THE BEST PART OF KUMBHA'S ARMY MUST BE WITH HIM, IT IS UNLIKELY THAT THE FEW MEN LEFT IN THE FORT CAN HOLD OUT FOR LONG.

BUT HE WAS IN FOR A SURPRISE.

A CLOUD OF DUST IN THE EAST! COULD IT BE...?

OH, IT IS KUMBHA!

THE SURPRISE ATTACK DEMORALISED THE FORCES OF MANDU.

I HAVE TRIED TIME AND AGAIN TO DEFEAT THE RANA. HE IS INVINCIBLE. I HAVE TO ACCEPT THIS BITTER TRUTH.

THEN THE SULTAN OF MANDU CALLED OUT TO HIS MEN.

TURN AROUND, MY MEN! RETREAT!

RANA KUMBHA WATCHED CONTENTEDLY AS THE SULTAN'S ARMY RETREATED.

HE WON'T TROUBLE US AGAIN. BUT EVEN IF HE DOES, WHAT DOES IT MATTER? AS LONG AS OUR PEOPLE ARE VIGILANT, THERE CAN BE NO THREAT TO OUR INDEPENDENCE.

THE STORY OF THE PEOPLE'S PRESIDENT: APJ ABDUL KALAM

RANA SANGA

THE VALIANT WARRIOR-KING

The route to your roots

RANA SANGA

Rana Sanga, the ruler of Mewar, had his eyes set on the throne of Delhi. However, the rising Mughal star Babur got rid of the Lodhi Sultan of Delhi. Thus the stage was set for the confrontation between the formidable Rana and an equally determined Babur who had just found a new home for his men – Hindustan.

Script
Rajendra Sanjay

Illustrations
Ram Waeerkar

Editor
Anant Pai

Cover illustration by: C.M. Vitankar

RANA SANGA

RANA RAIMAL, WHO RULED MEWAR IN THE EARLY HALF OF THE SIXTEENTH CENTURY, WAS A VALIANT KING WHO UPHELD THE GLORIOUS TRADITIONS OF HIS LAND. HIS THREE SONS, SANGA, PRITH-VIRAJ AND JAIMAL, HOWEVER, WERE FOR EVER INVOLVED IN PETTY QUARRELS WITH ONE ANOTHER.

THE DISUNITY OF OUR SONS WILL BE THE RUIN OF OUR KINGDOM.

BUT WHY DO THEY QUARREL SO?

1

EACH OF THEM WANTS TO BE MY SUCCESSOR.

BUT SANGA, THE ELDEST, HAS THE RIGHT TO THE THRONE.

THAT'S TRUE. THE PRINCES MIGHT HAVE ACCEPTED IT BUT FOR YOUR BROTHER, SURAJMAL. HE SETS THEM AGAINST ONE ANOTHER.

I CAN'T UNDERSTAND WHY HE DOES IT.

WHILE RAIMAL WORRIED, THE PRINCES CONTINUED TO QUARREL AND DRAW THEIR SWORDS AT THE SLIGHTEST PRETEXT.

I AM A BORN LEADER— BORN TO BE THE RULER OF MEWAR.

UNFORTUNATELY I AM THE RIGHTFUL HEIR, PRITHVIRAJ.

RIGHTFUL PERHAPS—BUT YOU ARE NOT FIT TO RULE, SANGA.

WHO SAYS SO?

I DO!

BEFORE SANGA COULD SAY ANYTHING, SURAJMAL CUT IN—

YOU FORGET ONE THING, PRITHVIRAJ— YOU HAVE NOT TAKEN INTO ACCOUNT THE WISHES OF THE PEOPLE.

WHAT CHANCE DO THE WISHES OF THE PEOPLE HAVE AGAINST MY MIGHT?

AS SANGA WAS ABOUT TO REPLY—

LET THE ORACLE, CHARANI DEVI, GUIDE US. HER PREDICTIONS NEVER GO WRONG.

THEY MOUNTED THEIR HORSES...

...AND SOON ARRIVED AT THE TEMPLE OF CHARANI DEVI.

WE HAVE COME TO CONSULT CHARANI DEVI.

WHAT DO YOU WANT TO KNOW?

WE'D LIKE TO KNOW WHICH OF US IS DESTINED TO RULE MEWAR.

PLEASE SIT DOWN. I WILL PUT THE QUESTION TO THE DEVI. SHE WILL GIVE YOU THE ANSWER THROUGH HER ATTENDANT.

SANGA, IF THE PREDICTION IS NOT IN YOUR FAVOUR, WHAT WILL YOU DO?

THE CALM AND PEACE OF THE TEMPLE HAD A STRANGE EFFECT ON SANGA. HE NO LONGER WANTED TO FIGHT WITH HIS BROTHERS.

I WILL GO AWAY AND ESTABLISH A NEW KINGDOM ELSEWHERE, IF MEWAR IS NOT DESTINED TO BE MINE.

AND IF IT IS, YOU WILL HAVE TO KILL ME FIRST.

MEANWHILE, THE PRIEST RETURNED WITH THE ATTENDANT WHO WAS THE MOUTHPIECE OF THE DEVI.

HERE THEY COME— WITH THE PREDICTION!

THE ATTENDANT POINTED TO THE TIGER SKIN ON WHICH SANGA WAS SITTING AND SURAJMAL WAS RESTING A KNEE.

THAT MEANS I AM TO RULE THE KINGDOM...

...OF WHICH I WILL ENJOY A SHARE.

SO THAT WAS THE JACKAL'S GAME!

BRISTLING WITH RAGE, PRITHVIRAJ DREW HIS SWORD AND CHARGED AT SANGA.

I WILL KILL THE LION FIRST AND THEN TACKLE THE JACKAL.

BUT SURAJMAL WHO LEAPT FORWARD TO PARRY THE THRUST...

...RECEIVED THE BLOW.

WHEN SANGA SAW THIS—

I WILL NOT INVOLVE MYSELF IN A FIGHT WITH MY BROTHER— AND CERTAINLY NOT IN THIS TEMPLE.

HE RAN OUT...

...AND MOUNTED HIS HORSE.

STOP SANGA! OR I'LL SHOOT YOU DOWN.

PRITHVIRAJ PULLED OUT AN ARROW AND TOOK AIM.

THE ARROW HIT SANGA IN ONE EYE, BLINDING IT FOR LIFE.

AH!

AS PRITHVIRAJ WAS ABOUT TO RUN UP TO SANGA AND FINISH HIM —

PRITHVIRAJ! STOP IT! FOR GOD'S SAKE!

THEN I WILL TAKE CARE OF YOU FIRST, UNCLE!

MEANWHILE —

PRITHVIRAJ'S ATTENTION IS DIVERTED. I'D BETTER ESCAPE.

WITH GREAT DIFFICULTY SANGA MANAGED TO REMOUNT HIS HORSE. AS HE WAS ABOUT TO RIDE AWAY —

JAIMAL! GO AFTER SANGA! DON'T LET HIM GET AWAY ALIVE!

DON'T WORRY, PRITHVIRAJ. I'LL FINISH HIM.

SANGA, STOP! I SAY STOP.

AT THAT MOMENT, VEEDA, A TRADESMAN WHO WAS PREPARING TO GO OUT OF MEWAR, WAS TAKING LEAVE OF HIS FAMILY. SUDDENLY—

THE PRINCES! THEY ARE COMING THIS WAY.

A FEW SECONDS LATER, UNABLE TO RIDE FURTHER, SANGA CAME TO A HALT IN FRONT OF VEEDA.

PRINCE SANGA! YOU ARE BADLY WOUNDED!

VEEDA HELPED SANGA DISMOUNT AND TURNED TO HIS WIFE—

QUICK! LEAD HIM TO MY HORSE, WHICH IS TIED BEHIND THE HOUSE. I'LL HANDLE JAIMAL.

10

A FEW SECONDS AFTER VEEDA'S WIFE LED SANGA AWAY, JAIMAL RODE UP.

WHERE IS SANGA?

I'LL GIVE UP MY LIFE BUT I'LL NEVER TELL YOU.

ENRAGED, JAIMAL DREW HIS SWORD AND ATTACKED VEEDA.

THIS SHOULD GIVE PRINCE SANGA ENOUGH TIME TO GET AWAY.

VEEDA STOPPED JAIMAL BUT AT THE COST OF HIS LIFE.

11

SANGA, MEANWHILE, ESCAPED ON VEEDA'S HORSE.

I WILL NOT GO BACK. PRITHVIRAJ IS DETERMINED TO TAKE THE THRONE. OUR WAR OVER THE SUCCESSION WILL BENEFIT NONE BUT THE ENEMIES OF MEWAR.

SO SANGA RODE AWAY FROM CHITTOR TOWARDS THE JUNGLES.

A FEW HOURS LATER, SANGA SAW SOME SHEPHERDS. HE APPROACHED THEM FOR WORK.

CAN YOU GRAZE OUR GOATS AND SHEEP AND COOK FOR US?

I WILL TRY.

AS A MENIAL, SANGA, THE PRINCE, WAS A FAILURE.

HE IS A GOOD-FOR-NOTHING!

IT'S NO USE KEEPING HIM.

FROM HIS WOUNDS I WOULD SAY HE IS A RUN-AWAY BANDIT.

SANGA SOON BECAME SICK AND TIRED OF THEIR STEADY ABUSE.

I MUST FIND SOME OTHER EMPLOYMENT.

BUT NOTHING CAME HIS WAY.

A FEW DAYS LATER—

ARMED HORSEMEN! THEY SEEM TO BE REBEL RAJPUTS.

WHO ARE YOU?

THEY HAVEN'T RECOGNISED ME. SHALL I ASK THEM TO GIVE ME SOME ARMS?

MY NAME IS SANGRAM SINGH. I TOO AM A RAJPUT. BUT I HAVE NO ARMS EVEN FOR MY OWN PROTECTION.

WE'LL GIVE YOU ARMS. WHY DON'T YOU JOIN US?

WITH PLEASURE!

MY LUCK SEEMS TO HAVE TURNED.

COME, THEN. WE'LL TAKE YOU TO OUR CHIEF.

SANGA WAS INTRODUCED TO THEIR CHIEF, KARAM CHAND.

THIS BRAVE RAJPUT, SANGRAM SINGH, WISHES TO WORK WITH US.

LET'S HOPE YOU MAKE A GOOD DACOIT.

OH! SO THEY'RE REBELS WHO HAVE TURNED DACOITS.

AS SANGA HESITATED, KARAM CHAND'S DAUGHTER CAME OUT—

TAKE SANGRAM IN AND ATTEND TO HIS NEEDS.

YES, FATHER.

SANGA AND KARAM CHAND'S DAUGHTER SOON FELL IN LOVE WITH EACH OTHER. ONE DAY—

WHAT ARE YOU DOING HERE ALONE?

THINKING!

WHAT ARE YOU THINKING ABOUT?

I DO NOT LIKE THE LIFE I'M LEADING.

NEITHER DO I.

THEN WHY DON'T YOU MARRY ME AND COME AWAY WITH ME?

MARU, ONE OF THE REBELS, OVERHEARD THEIR CONVERSATION AND TOLD KARAM CHAND ABOUT IT.

SO SANGRAM HAS NO TASTE FOR OUR WAY OF LIFE. HM.M..!

KARAM CHAND ASKED MARU TO KEEP A CLOSE WATCH ON SANGA. A FEW DAYS LATER—

WHAT IS IT, MARU?

COME OUT AND SEE FOR YOURSELF, SIR. IT'S UNBELIEVABLE!

THIS MEANS THAT SANGRAM IS GOING TO BE A KING.

DON'T SPEAK OF THIS TO ANYONE. NOT EVEN TO SANGRAM.

MY DAUGHTER COULD NOT HAVE MADE A BETTER CHOICE.

THE NEXT DAY—

I'VE HEARD YOU DON'T LIKE OUR WAY OF LIFE.

YOUR DAUGHTER DOES NOT LIKE IT EITHER!

HOW DO YOU KNOW?

SHE TOLD ME.

SO YOU HAVE BEEN MEETING EACH OTHER!

YES. WE HAVE. I WANT TO MARRY HER.

YOU HAVE MY CONSENT BUT PROMISE ME YOU WILL NOT MAKE HER UNHAPPY.

YOU CAN TRUST ME.

AFTER THE WEDDING, SANGA AND HIS BRIDE APPROACHED KARAM CHAND FOR HIS BLESSINGS.

SANGRAM, I APPOINT YOU NAIK OF MY BAND.

I CANNOT ACCEPT. I AM DESTINED TO RULE OVER MEWAR.

RULE OVER MEWAR! ISN'T THAT A VAIN HOPE?

NOT FOR RANA SANGA, THE ELDEST SON OF RANA RAIMAL!

RANA SANGA?

YES. I AM RANA SANGA. BUT I WANT YOU TO KEEP MY SECRET AND GIVE ME PROTECTION TILL I KNOW WHAT THE SITUATION IS LIKE IN CHITTOR.

WE WILL SEND SOMEONE TO FIND OUT.

THE MESSENGER RETURNED WITH INTERESTING NEWS. SANGA'S BAD DAYS WERE OVER. PRITHVIRAJ AND JAIMAL WERE NO MORE.

THE KING'S MEN ARE LOOKING FOR YOU EVERYWHERE.

GO TO CHITTOR. DON'T WASTE ANOTHER MOMENT.

MEANWHILE, AT CHITTOR—

TWO SONS KILLED, AND SANGA NOT YET TRACED.

WHO WILL SUCCEED ME? WHAT WILL BECOME OF MY KINGDOM.

HAVE PATIENCE, SIR. OUR MEN ARE LOOKING EVERYWHERE FOR...

18

AT THAT MOMENT—

MAHARAJ KI JAI! PRINCE SANGA IS HERE!

MY SON! WHERE IS MY SON?

WHERE IS HE?

GOD HAS GRANTED OUR PRAYERS!

SON, WHERE WERE YOU ALL THIS TIME?

WHAT DOES IT MATTER? HE IS HERE NOW.

YES. I AM HERE, ALIVE AND WELL!

SOON AFTERWARDS, RAIMAL DIED AND SANGA BECAME KING. WITHIN A FEW YEARS, MEWAR REACHED THE SUMMIT OF PROSPERITY. ONE DAY AT COURT—

IBRAHIM LODI'S POWER IS ALREADY ON THE DECLINE.

WE CAN VANQUISH THE SULTAN WITHOUT MUCH DIFFICULTY!

TO WIN DELHI IS TO RULE THE WHOLE COUNTRY!

SULTAN, I WILL NOT LET YOU ESCAPE!

THE SULTAN WAS SOON CAPTURED.

HIS ARMY HAD FLED.

THOUGH A PRISONER, MAHMOOD KHILJI WAS TREATED LIKE AN HONOURED GUEST.

WHY DO YOU TREAT ME, A PRISONER, SO ROYALLY?

BECAUSE YOU ARE A KING AND A GUEST IN MY PALACE.

I COULD EASILY ESCAPE.

THAT WOULD BE COWARDLY.

KHILJI HAD TO CEDE FOUR PROVINCES — BHILSA, SARANGPUR, CHANDERI AND RANTHAMBOR — BEFORE SANGA RELEASED HIM. MEANWHILE, BABAR HAD INVADED DELHI.

BABAR IS JUST ANOTHER PLUNDERER!

IF HE DEFEATS LODI, HE WILL COLLECT ALL THE WEALTH HE CAN AND GO BACK!

AND IF HE STAYS ON, IT WON'T MAKE ANY DIFFERENCE TO US.

HIS NEW REGIME WILL NOT BE STRONG ENOUGH TO RESIST US.

WHETHER WE FIGHT LODI OR BABAR — IT IS ALL THE SAME TO US.

WE MUST TAKE OVER DELHI AT ALL COSTS.

IN APRIL 1526, BABAR DEFEATED IBRAHIM LODI, BECAME THE NEW RULER OF DELHI AND IMMEDIATELY MADE PREPARATIONS FOR A WAR ON CHITTOR. SANGA HELD COUNCIL WITH HIS MINISTERS.

AMAZING! BABAR HAS COMPLETED HIS PREPARA-TIONS!

HE SEEMS TO BE AMBI-TIOUS.

ALL BRAVE MEN ARE AMBITIOUS. SHILA-DITYA, OUR FORCES HAVE TO BE FURTHER STRENGTH-ENED.

HE SHOULD BE DRIVEN OUT OF OUR MOTHER-LAND.

I LIKE YOUR SPIRIT, SHILADITYA. I PUT YOU IN CHARGE OF THE DEFENCE UNITS.

WE TRUST YOU TO PERFORM YOUR TASK WITH HONOUR AND SINCERITY.

I WILL NOT HESITATE TO LAY DOWN MY LIFE IN DOING MY DUTY.

MEANWHILE, AT BABAR'S COURT IN DELHI—

JAHANPANAH, WE WILL RUN A GREAT RISK IN FIGHT-ING RANA SANGA.

OUR SOLDIERS ARE OVERAWED BY THE VALOUR OF THE RAJPUTS.

LET US TEST THE METTLE OF THIS MAN WHO HAS ONLY ONE EYE AND ONE ARM.

IN MARCH 1527, BABAR ATTACKED. THE FORCES OF RANA SANGA AND BABAR MET IN THE BATTLEFIELD OF KHANWA.

BABAR'S ADVANCE OF ABOUT 1500 MEN WAS CUT TO PIECES.

REINFORCEMENTS WERE SENT BUT THEY TOO MADE A HURRIED RETREAT.

JAHANPANAH, OUR SOLDIERS HAVE ALREADY LOST HEART.

I WILL SPEAK TO THEM.

BABAR ORDERED THE DESTRUCTION OF ALL WINE FLASKS.

I VOW NEVER TO DRINK WINE AGAIN.

THEN HE MADE A STIRRING SPEECH BEFORE HIS SOLDIERS.

...BY THE HOLY KORAN, VICTORY WILL BE OURS.

I HOPE I DO NOT HAVE TO SUE FOR PEACE.

ON THE SECOND DAY OF THE BATTLE, HOWEVER, BABAR SENT HIS EMISSARY TO RANA SANGA.

WE WILL ACCEPT BABAR'S PEACE PROPOSAL— ON OUR TERMS.

BUT BABAR REJECTED THE TERMS. A LITTLE LATER—

JEHANPANAH, RANA SANGA'S EMISSARY IS HERE.

BRING HIM IN WITH DUE HONOUR.

ACCEPT OUR TERMS. IT IS NOT POSSIBLE TO DEFEAT SANGA'S ARMY.

YOU CAN MAKE IT POSSIBLE.

WHAT DO YOU MEAN?

IF WE JOIN HANDS, WE CAN BOTH GET WHAT WE WANT!

YOU MEAN YOU WIN THE WAR.

AND YOU GET CHITTOR!

GREED GOT THE BETTER OF SHILADITYA.

YOU WON'T GO BACK ON YOUR WORD, WILL YOU?

ON THE HOLY KORAN— I WILL NOT.

AS SOON AS SHILADITYA RETURNED TO HIS CAMP—

THE RANA HAS BEEN ASKING FOR YOU.

I'LL GO TO HIM.

IS MY SECRET ALREADY KNOWN?

27

FOR THAT VERY REASON YOU WILL LEAD THE FRONTAL ATTACK, SHILADITYA. I WILL LEAD THE REAR ATTACK.

I WILL ASTONISH YOU WITH MY PROWESS.

I HAVE COMPLETE FAITH IN YOU.

IN THE DARK NIGHT, SANGA LEFT FOR THE HILL WITH HIS TROOPS.

BOTH ARMIES ARE GETTING READY.

MOTHER CHANDI IS MY WITNESS— WE WILL WIN.

THIS WILL BE THE DECISIVE DAY.

THE TWO ARMIES SOON FACED EACH OTHER.

SUDDENLY—

LOOK! LOOK! INSTEAD OF FIGHTING, THE TWO ARMIES ARE MARCHING TOWARDS CHITTOR TOGETHER.

WE HAVE BEEN BETRAYED. SHILADITYA, I TRUSTED YOU...

SINCE THE MAJOR PART OF HIS ARMY HAD BEEN GIVEN TO SHILADITYA, RANA SANGA HAD TO ABANDON HIS PLANS.

A REAR ATTACK WOULD NOW BE IN VAIN.

RANA SANGA AND HIS MEN WANDERED INTO THE HILLS, AWAITING AN OPPORTUNITY TO ATTACK THE MUGHALS.

I VOW NOT TO RETURN TO MEWAR UNTIL I'VE VANQUISHED THE MUGHALS.

WE ARE WITH YOU.

BUT THE UNCERTAINTY AND INSECURITY OF LIFE IN EXILE AFFECTED THE RANA'S HEALTH.

HE WAS CONFINED TO BED AND WAS UNABLE TO FULFIL HIS VOW.

WILL YOU FORGIVE YOUR DEFAULTING SON, O MOTHER-LAND?

A FEW MONTHS LATER, HE DIED AT VASVA, A VILLAGE IN THE HILLS.

IF SHILADITYA HAD NOT BETRAYED RANA SANGA, INDIA PERHAPS WOULD HAVE BEEN SAVED THE HUMILIATION OF FOREIGN DOMINATION.

31

Amar Chitra Katha's

EPICS & MYTHOLOGY

BRAVEHEARTS

VISIONARIES

FABLES & HUMOUR

INDIAN CLASSICS

CONTEMPORARY CLASSICS

EXCITING STORY CATEGORIES, ONE AMAZING DESTINATION.

From the episodes of Mahabharata to the wit of Birbal,
from the valour of Shivaji to the teachings of Tagore,
from the adventures of Pratapan to the tales of Ruskin Bond –
Amar Chitra Katha stories span across different genres to get you the best of literature.

To buy/view our products go to
www.amarchitrakatha.com

RANA PRATAP

HE FOUGHT FOR FREEDOM

The route to your roots

RANA PRATAP

Disdaining even the comfort of a bed, the valiant Rana Pratap waged a single-minded, life-long war against the mighty Mughal conquerors. His Rajput pride instilled a deep respect in the enemy. They realised that huge armies and sophisticated weapons are but aids, and that there can be no substitute for raw courage on the battlefield.

Script	Illustrations	Editor
Yagya Sharma	Pratap Mulick	Anant Pai

Rana Pratap

RAJASTHAN IN WESTERN INDIA WAS THE HOME OF THE VALIANT RAJPUTS.

1

THROUGHOUT HISTORY, THEY HAD REPEATEDLY FOUGHT FOR THE HONOUR OF THE COUNTRY.

BUT THE RAJPUTS OF CHITTOR SURPASSED ALL, IN DEEDS OF BRAVERY AND PERSONAL SACRIFICE.

IN THE EIGHTH CENTURY A.D. THEY REPULSED AN INVASION OF THEIR LAND.

AND THEIR WOMEN WERE NO LESS HEROIC. CHITTOR'S QUEEN KARMA DEVI HAD DEFEATED THE POWERFUL HORDES OF QUTAB-UD-DIN.

IN THE 14TH CENTURY, QUEEN PADMINI AND HUNDREDS OF RAJPUT WOMEN OF CHITTOR PERFORMED SATI, AN ACT OF SELF-IMMOLATION TO SAVE THEIR HONOUR FROM THE INVADER, ALA-UD-DIN KHILJI.

THE MUGHALS WERE THE FIRST INVADERS WHO SUCCEEDED IN OCCUPYING CHITTOR.

ALMOST ALL MAJOR RAJPUT KINGS HAD SURRENDERED TO THE ENEMY BUT RANA PRATAP, THE KING OF CHITTOR, REFUSED TO.

I SWEAR THAT I WILL SACRIFICE MY VERY LIFE FOR CHITTOR.

WE ALSO PLEDGE THAT TILL WE ATTAIN FREEDOM, WE WILL NOT SLEEP ON A BED BUT ON THE GROUND AND WE WILL NOT WEAR FANCY CLOTHES.

MAY GODDESS KALI BLESS YOU RANAJI, YOU HAVE TAKEN A TERRIBLE OATH.

GURUDEV, DEFENDING ONE'S MOTHERLAND IS A SERIOUS MATTER...

... AND NO SACRIFICE IS TOO BIG FOR SUCH A NOBLE CAUSE.

WE WILL FIGHT FOR FREEDOM WITH THE LAST DROP OF OUR BLOOD.

WELL SAID. BUT OUR TASK IS A DIFFICULT ONE. MANY OF OUR OWN PEOPLE ARE HELPING THE INVADERS.

WE MUST INCREASE OUR STRENGTH. LET'S CAPTURE AN IMPORTANT FORT FIRST.

SO, A HANDFUL OF RANA PRATAP'S WARRIORS ATTACKED A FORT, UNDER MUGHAL OCCUPATION, NEAR CHITTOR.

HAR HAR MAHADEV!

JAI CHANDI!

FINALLY THE MUGHAL FORCES WERE DEFEATED.

WELL DONE, MY MEN! THE FORT IS OURS.

THIS VICTORY BROUGHT MANY RAJPUTS FROM CHITTOR TO THE FORT TO JOIN PRATAP'S FORCES.

TELL THE PEOPLE OF CHITTOR THAT THOUGH THEY ARE RULED BY THE INVADERS...

...I AM THEIR TRUE KING. I ORDER THAT NOBODY SHALL TILL THE LAND TILL WE ATTAIN FREEDOM.

MEANWHILE, IN THE COURT OF AKBAR —

HAVE YOU HEARD THE LATEST JOKE? PRATAP STILL CALLS HIMSELF THE KING OF CHITTOR.

OF COURSE, HE IS A KING BUT WITHOUT A KINGDOM.

SILENCE! YOU FORGET THAT PRATAP HAS TAKEN A FORT.

BUT SIR, OUR HUGE ARMY CAN CRUSH HIM IN NO TIME.

YOU ARE WRONG. IT IS NOT GOING TO BE EASY TO CRUSH PRATAP.

MEANWHILE IN RANA PRATAP'S FORT –

RANAJI! THIS MAN WAS TILLING HIS LAND.

WHY DID YOU DISOBEY MY ORDERS?

BUT I HAD TAKEN THE PERMISSION OF THE MUGHAL GOVERNOR.

I AM THE KING OF CHITTOR AND I HAVE NOT GIVEN YOU THE PERMISSION...

...YOUR CROP WILL FINALLY FEED THE ENEMY AND THUS HELP HIM.

FOR ACTING AGAINST THE INTEREST OF OUR MOTHER-LAND, YOU SHALL DIE!

THE FOLLOWING DAY, THE FARMER WAS HANGED.

THE NEWS OF THE FARMER'S DEATH REACHED AKBAR.

THIS IS OUTRAGEOUS. PERHAPS HE CAN STILL BE WON OVER.

AKBAR CONSULTED HIS RAJPUT COMMANDER, MAN SINGH.

A BRAVE MAN LIKE PRATAP SHOULD BE OUR FRIEND, RAJA MAN SINGH. PLEASE GO AND ASK HIM TO STOP THIS REVOLT AGAINST US.

YOU ARE RIGHT, SIR. HIS FRIENDSHIP CAN BE AN ASSET TO THE MUGHAL EMPIRE.

AND SO MAN SINGH WENT TO MEET RANA PRATAP. HE WAS RECEIVED BY PRATAP'S MINISTER.

WELCOME, SIR, MAN SINGH!

I HAVE A MESSAGE. MAHARAJ AKBAR, THE KING OF BHARAT, SEEKS RANAJI'S FRIENDSHIP.

HE MAY BE A KING FOR YOU, BUT TO US HE IS AN INVADER, AN ENEMY.

IT IS TREASON TO RISE AGAINST THE KING.

IT IS NOT TREASON BUT OUR SACRED DUTY TO FIGHT FOR OUR FREEDOM.

BUT WHY DON'T YOU REALISE THAT YOU CAN'T DEFEAT OUR HUGE FORCES.

WE SHALL DO OUR DUTY WHETHER WE WIN OR NOT.

RANA PRATAP ENTERED WITH HIS SON, AMAR SINGH.

THAT IS ENOUGH FOR NOW, MINISTER WE WILL DISCUSS THE MATTER LATER. RAJA MAN SINGH MUST BE HUNGRY. LET US OFFER HIM OUR SIMPLE FOOD, AMAR.

YES FATHER!

WON'T YOU JOIN ME?

NO, YOU ARE OUR GUEST. SO, YOU MUST EAT BEFORE US.

BUT THE HOST MUST ALSO EAT WITH THE GUEST.

I AM SORRY, BUT I CAN'T EAT WITH YOU.

MAY I KNOW WHY?

SOON AFTER MAN SINGH LEFT, RANA PRATAP ATTACKED A CAMP OF MUGHAL FORCES AND KILLED MANY OF THEM.

IN THE COURT OF AKBAR—

PRATAP HAS LEFT US NO OTHER ALTERNATIVE. WE WILL HAVE TO CRUSH HIM.

VERY WELL, THEN DO IT.

SOON MAN SINGH AND PRINCE SALIM SET OUT WITH A HUGE ARMY.

IF WE CAN DRIVE PRATAP OUT OF HIS FORT, THEN OUR TASK WILL BECOME EASY.

YES, WITH OUR LARGE ARMY WE CAN DEFEAT HIM.

FINALLY AKBAR'S FORCES REACHED THE FAMOUS BATTLE-GROUND, HALDI-GHATI, SITUATED IN A NARROW VALLEY.

NOW BEGINS THE TOUGHEST PART OF OUR JOB.

MEANWHILE IN PRATAP'S FORT—

RANAJI, OUR SCOUTS HAVE BROUGHT NEWS THAT THE ENEMY HAS 80,000 MEN WITH CANNONS AND GUNS.

AND WE HAVE ONLY 22,000 SOLDIERS AND NO GUNS.

I WISH I HAD SOME CANNONS AND MORE SOLDIERS.

MAN SINGH ALSO RECEIVED VITAL INFORMATION.

COMMANDER MAN SINGH, PRATAP HAS ONLY 22,000 SOLDIERS AND THEY HAVE NO GUNS.

THAT IS GOOD NEWS.

THIS MAN PRATAP MUST BE STUPID TO CHALLENGE THE MUGHAL EMPIRE WITHOUT ENOUGH SOLDIERS AND GOOD WEAPONS.

BRAVE, NOT STUPID! HE IS A TRUE RAJPUT AND...

...DON'T BE OVERCONFIDENT, PRINCE. HUGE ARMIES AND GOOD WEAPONS DO HELP IN A BATTLE. BUT WHEN IT COMES TO FIGHTING, THERE IS NO SUBSTITUTE FOR COURAGE.

GOOD, TAKE ENOUGH SOLDIERS AND ATTACK THE FORT FROM THE REAR.

YES SIR!

AND A STRONG MUGHAL FORCE MARCHED OFF TO SURROUND RANA PRATAP'S FORT.

WHEN RANA PRATAP HEARD ABOUT THIS NEW TROOP MOVEMENT, HE WAS WORRIED.

THE BEST STRATEGY WOULD HAVE BEEN TO FIGHT FROM THE FORT BUT NOW WE HAVE TO FACE THEM IN HALDI-GHATI.

FINALLY IN THE VALLEY CALLED HALDI-GHATI —

ATTACK!

PRATAP AND HIS SOLDIERS CHARGED FIERCELY.

EVEN PRATAP'S FAITHFUL HORSE CHETAK PARTICIPATED IN THE BATTLE.

THE MUGHAL FORCES SUFFERED HEAVY LOSSES.

BUT JUST WHEN THE MUGHALS STARTED TO LOSE, MORE OF THEIR TROOPS ARRIVED.

IN THE BITTER FIGHTING THAT FOLLOWED, RANA PRATAP LOST 15,000 MEN.

BUT THE BATTLE CONTINUED.

MAN SINGH IS AN ABLE COMMANDER. IF HE IS KILLED, HIS FORCES WILL LOSE THEIR MORALE.

RANA PRATAP ADVANCED TOWARDS MAN SINGH.

MAN SINGH WAS RIDING AN ELEPHANT. PRATAP ATTACKED HIM LIKE A FIERCE LION.

PRATAP THREW HIS SPEAR AT MAN SINGH, BUT JUST THEN THE ELEPHANT MOVED AND PRATAP MISSED HIS MARK. MAN SINGH WAS SAVED.

MEANWHILE PRATAP WAS SURROUNDED BY ENEMY SOLDIERS.

FINDING THEIR LEADER IN DANGER, PRATAP'S FRIEND, MANA AND A FEW SOLDIERS RUSHED TO HIS RESCUE.

OUR RANA IS WOUNDED. I MUST SAVE HIM.

TO SAVE PRATAP, MANA PLACED PRATAP'S HELMET ON HIS OWN HEAD.

THE MUGHAL SOLDIERS WERE FOOLED. THEY ATTACKED MANA, MISTAKING HIM FOR PRATAP. WHILE MANA FACED THE ENEMY, PRATAP WAS CARRIED AWAY BY HIS FAITHFUL HORSE, CHETAK.

SOME RAJPUT SOLDIERS RODE WITH CHETAK TO PROTECT THE UNCONSCIOUS RANA.

THE WOUNDED PRATAP WAS TAKEN TO A CAVE IN THE JUNGLES.

THOUGH PRATAP SURVIVED, HIS FAMILY HAD A HARD TIME. FOR SEVERAL DAYS THEY HAD NOTHING TO EAT BUT WILD BERRIES AND ROOTS.

ONE DAY, WHEN PRATAP'S SON, AMAR SINGH, WAS EATING A DRY CHAPATI...

FATHER, THE CAT SNATCHED MY CHAPATI.

PRATAP'S DAUGHTER, WHO GAVE HER CHAPATI TO HER BROTHER, FAINTED DUE TO HUNGER.

I CAN'T BEAR IT ANY MORE. I SHALL WRITE TO AKBAR.

SOME TIME LATER, IN AKBAR'S COURT —

AT LAST RANA PRATAP HAS DECIDED TO BOW DOWN TO ME. THIS IS AN OCCASION FOR CELEBRATION.

PRITHVIRAJ, A RAJPUT POET IN AKBAR'S COURT, WAS A SECRET ADMIRER OF PRATAP. HE DID NOT LIKE THE NEWS.

SO THE LAST HOPE OF FREEDOM IS ALSO LOST. I MUST DO SOMETHING ABOUT IT.

AND POET PRITHVIRAJ SENT A LETTER TO RANA PRATAP.

You alone can preserve the honour of the Rajputs. The sun would sooner rise in the west than have you address Akbar as your Lord.

INSPIRING WORDS! I MUST WRITE TO HIM THAT THE SUN WILL CONTINUE TO RISE IN THE EAST. I WILL NEVER BOW BEFORE AKBAR.

UNAWARE OF PRITHVIRAJ'S LETTER, AKBAR SENT A LARGE BAND OF SOLDIERS TO ESCORT PRATAP FROM THE JUNGLES.

WHEN RANA PRATAP REFUSED TO GO WITH THEM, THE SOLDIERS ATTACKED HIM.

WE ARE GREATLY OUTNUMBERED.

FIGHT, MY BRAVE MEN!

SOON ALL THE RAJPUT SOLDIERS WERE KILLED AND PRATAP WAS ABOUT TO BE CAPTURED, WHEN A BAND OF BHIL TRIBALS ATTACKED THE MUGHALS.

THE BHILS RESCUED PRATAP AND HIS FAMILY AND CARRIED THEM TO THEIR VILLAGE. PRATAP WAS SAD OVER THE LOSS OF HIS SOLDIERS.

EVERYTHING IS FINISHED NOW. I CAN'T LIBERATE MY MOTHER-LAND.

YOU SHOULDN'T LOSE HEART, RANAJI. YOU ARE OUR ONLY HOPE.

BUT WITHOUT AN ARMY HOW CAN I FACE THE MUGHALS?

I WILL COLLECT MY TRIBESMEN FROM THE JUNGLE AND THEN YOU CAN FIGHT AGAIN.

BUT FOR RAISING AN ARMY WE NEED MONEY AND I HAVE NONE.

ONE DAY—

I CAN'T REMAIN A BURDEN ON YOU ANY MORE. I SHALL GO AWAY FROM HERE.

YOU ARE NOT A BURDEN, RANAJI.

JUST THEN A MESSENGER ARRIVED.

RANAJI, A PERSON CALLED BHAMA SHAH WANTS TO MEET YOU.

BRING HIM IN.

RANAJI, I HEARD THAT YOU NEED MONEY. MY WEALTH IS AT YOUR DISPOSAL.

BUT I CAN'T ACCEPT YOUR PERSONAL PROPERTY.

BHAMA SHAH WAS A PROMINENT BUSINESSMAN OF CHITTOR.

NOTHING REMAINS PERSONAL WHEN OUR COUNTRY IS IN TROUBLE NOW EVERYTHING BELONGS TO THE COUNTRY.

WITH THE HELP OF THIS HUGE WEALTH, PRATAP RAISED A POWERFUL ARMY OF BHILS.

NOW, WE ARE PREPARED TO FIGHT THE MUGHALS AGAIN.

JAI CHANDI! HAR HAR MAHADEV!

PRATAP LED THE BRAVE BHILS TO MANY VICTORIES.

THE FORT OF PHINSAHRA WAS WON FROM THE MUGHALS.

THEN PRATAP SWIFTLY ATTACKED OTHER NEARBY FORTS UNDER MUGHAL OCCUPATION.

FINALLY RANA PRATAP MANAGED TO LIBERATE THE AREAS OF DEVAR, UDAIPUR AND KOMALMIR.

BUT CHITTOR WAS STILL OCCUPIED BY THE MUGHALS. PRATAP HAD FOUGHT RELENTLESSLY FOR TWENTY YEARS. NOW HE WAS VERY SICK.

SOON YOU WOULD BE HEALTHY AGAIN, RANAJI!

NO, I KNOW THAT MY END HAS COME.

HOW UNLUCKY I AM THAT I COULD NOT LIBERATE MY MOTHER-LAND, CHITTOR.

THUS WITH HIS DREAM ONLY PARTIALLY FULFILLED, RANA PRATAP PASSED AWAY. TILL THE LAST DAY OF HIS LIFE, HE STRICTLY ADHERED TO HIS OATH. EVEN WHEN HE WAS SICK, HE DID NOT SLEEP ON A COMFORTABLE BED, BUT ON THE GROUND. THUS RANA PRATAP SET AN EXAMPLE TO LEADERS OF ALL TIMES THAT THEY HAD NO RIGHT TO LIVE IN LUXURY WHEN THE COUNTRY SUFFERED.

RANI DURGAVATI

THE BRAVE AND WISE QUEEN

The route to your roots

RANI
DURGAVATI

She chose to be the wife of a brave, 'low-born' hero, rather than of a spineless 'high-born' fool. This was indeed fortunate for the people of Garha, for they gained a queen who could befuddle even the mightiest of Mughal armies. Her intelligence and courage were unmatched. But this made the Mughal general, Asaf Khan, all the more determined to subdue her.

Script
Kamala Chandrakant

Illustrations
Ram Waeerkar

Editor
Anant Pai

Cover illustration by: C.M.Vitankar

RANI DURGAVATI

DURGAVATI WAS THE DAUGHTER OF THE RAJPUT CHIEF OF MAHOBA,* A POWERFUL RAJPUT KINGDOM. SHE RODE WELL, WAS A GOOD SHOT AND OFTEN WENT OUT HUNTING WITH HER FATHER.

ONE DAY, AS THEY RODE TOWARDS THE JUNGLES—

FATHER, I HEAR MUCH TALK ABOUT THE BRAVE, HEROIC DALPAT SHAH. WHO IS HE?

HE IS THE SON OF SANGRAM SHAH, THE GOND RULER OF GARHA.

A PRINCE?

YES. BUT OF LOW ORIGIN.

1

HIS ANCESTOR JADURAI WAS IN THE SERVICE OF THE KALACHURI RAJA OF GARHA.

I SEE. THEN?

JADURAI MARRIED THE DAUGHTER OF A GOND CHIEFTAIN TO GIVE HIMSELF POWER AND STATUS...

... TO OVERTHROW THE RAJPUT RULER.

HM—M—M.

THAT WAS HOW THE GONDS WRESTED THE POWER FROM THE HANDS OF OUR ANCESTORS WHO HAD RULED THE LAND FOR CENTURIES.

DURGAVATI WAS THOUGHTFUL FOR A WHILE. THEN—

WELL, FATHER, IT IS NO EASY TASK TO SUBDUE OUR PEOPLE. THE GONDS MUST BE A BRAVE AND POWERFUL RACE.

DURGAVATI SEEMS TO THINK VERY HIGHLY OF DALPAT AND THE GONDS.

MEANWHILE AT GARHA —

ARE YOU READY, DALPAT?

YES, FATHER. LET'S GO.

I AM IMPATIENT TO SEE YOUR ARROWS EMBEDDED IN THE TIGER'S FLESH.

AFTER THEY HAD RIDDEN SOME DISTANCE —

LOOK OUT, DALPAT. THERE HE IS.

BUT EVEN BEFORE SANGRAM COULD SPEAK, DALPAT HAD RAISED HIS BOW.

HE SENT THE ARROW FLYING.

SANGRAM'S HEART SWELLED WITH PRIDE.

MY HANDSOME, DARING, MANLY SON. YOU SHALL MARRY A PRINCESS WORTHY OF YOU.

I CAN THINK OF NO BETTER MATCH THAN DURGAVATI, THE PRINCESS OF MAHOBA.

SANGRAM SHAH SENT A PROPOSAL TO DURGAVATI'S FATHER.

IT WOULD BE AN HONOUR FOR US TO ENTER INTO AN ALLIANCE WITH YOUR PEOPLE. I SEEK THE HAND OF YOUR DAUGHTER, THE FAIR DURGAVATI, FOR MY SON, DALPAT.
— SANGRAM SHAH

DALPAT IS A PRINCE, NO DOUBT. BUT A PRINCESS OF THE FAMOUS CHANDELA DYNASTY TO MARRY A MERE GOND? NO! NEVER! IT MAY BE AN HONOUR FOR YOU, SANGRAM SHAH. BUT IT WOULD MEAN DISGRACE FOR OUR FAMILY.

AND DURGAVATI'S FATHER REPLIED, EXPRESSING HIS REGRETS.

TAKE THIS TO YOUR CHIEF.

MEANWHILE, THE MAID RAN TO DURGAVATI.

YOUR HAND HAS BEEN SOUGHT BY THE GOND RULER FOR HIS SON.

DALPAT?

YES!

WHAT DID MY FATHER SAY?

THE MAID SHOOK HER HEAD SADLY.

HE WAS VERY UNKIND.

HOW? WHAT DID HE SAY? WHAT DID HE DO?

HE SAID... HE SAID... IT WOULD BE A DISGRACE TO GIVE A DAUGHTER OF THE FAMOUS CHANDELA DYNASTY TO A GOND, PRINCE THOUGH HE BE.

MY FATHER IS WRONG. A MAN SHOULD BE JUDGED, NOT BY HIS BIRTH, BUT BY HIS CHARACTER AND ACHIEVEMENTS.

AS DURGAVATI WALKED TOWARDS THE PALACE, SHE MADE A DECISION.

I WILL MARRY DALPAT, COME WHAT MAY! IT IS BETTER TO BE THE WIFE OF A BRAVE, LOW-BORN HERO THAN OF A SPINELESS, HIGH-BORN FOOL!

SHE WROTE TO DALPAT.

...SOCIAL BARRIERS ARE ABSURD. IN YOU I HAVE FOUND A HERO AFTER MY OWN HEART. IT IS MY SINCERE HOPE THAT YOU WILL PERSIST IN YOUR EFFORTS TO WIN MY HAND...

SHE TURNED TO THE MAID.

TAKE THIS TO THE SON OF THE GOND RULER. AND... AND... BE DISCREET ABOUT IT.

YOU CAN TRUST ME TO DO THAT, MISTRESS.

MEANWHILE, AT GARHA, NEWS OF THE MAHOBA CHIEF'S REBUFF HAD ALREADY REACHED DALPAT.

WHAT UTTER HUMILIATION! OH, FATHER! WHY DID WE HAVE TO DEMEAN OURSELVES SO?

THERE ARE MANY GOOD GIRLS AMONG OUR OWN PEOPLE. I COULD HAVE MARRIED ONE OF THEM. WHY, O WHY, DID YOU BOW BEFORE THAT HAUGHTY RAJPUT?

AS HE BROODED THUS, THE MAID CAME THERE.

SIR, A MESSAGE FROM MY MISTRESS — DURGAVATI, THE PRINCESS OF MAHOBA.

DALPAT READ THE NOTE.

MY FATHER, AFTER ALL, CHOSE NO ORDINARY PRINCESS.

WHAT SHALL I TELL MY MISTRESS, SIR?

TELL HER I SHALL COME.

I WILL, SIR. I WILL.

WHEN THE MAID LEFT, DALPAT WENT TO SANGRAM.

FATHER, I HAVE DECIDED TO MAKE DURGAVATI MY WIFE. WITH HER FATHER'S CONSENT, IF POSSIBLE; WITHOUT IF NECESSARY.

SANGRAM WAS DELIGHTED.

I SHALL ORDER OUR MEN TO GET READY TO MARCH INTO MAHOBA.

LATER, AT MAHOBA —

SIR! SIR! THE GONDS ARE ON THE WARPATH. THEIR PRINCE RIDES THIS WAY AT THE HEAD OF A HUGE ARMY.

THE RAJPUT CHIEF WAS SILENT FOR A WHILE.

IT WOULD BE MORE DIS-CREET TO HAND DURGAVATI OVER PEACEFULLY, THOUGH IT WILL MEAN LOSS OF FACE FOR ME.

THEN HE GAVE ORDERS.

PUT UP THE TRUCE FLAGS. I WILL GO OUT AND WELCOME THE GOND PRINCE. HE IS DURGAVATI'S CHOSEN LORD.

AS YOU SAY, SIR.

THE ORDERS WERE CARRIED OUT.

DALPAT WAS GIVEN A ROYAL WELCOME.

DALPAT, YOU HAVE WON. DURGAVATI SHALL BECOME YOUR BRIDE.

THEN AMIDST GREAT FEASTING AND REJOICING, DURGAVATI WAS MARRIED TO DALPAT.

A FEW DAYS LATER, WITH THE BLESSINGS OF HIS FATHER-IN-LAW, DALPAT SET OUT FOR GARHA WITH HIS BRIDE.

SANGRAM SHAH WAS WAITING IMPATIENTLY TO RECEIVE THEM.

DEAR DAUGHTER, WELCOME TO GARHA. FROM NOW ON DALPAT SHALL RULE THE KINGDOM WITH YOU BY HIS SIDE. MY PEOPLE ARE FORTUNATE TO HAVE YOU FOR THEIR QUEEN.

THEIR HAPPINESS AND WELL-BEING SHALL EVER BE MY CONCERN, FATHER.

A YEAR LATER, A SON WAS BORN TO THE HAPPY YOUNG COUPLE.

WE SHALL NAME HIM BIR NARAYAN.

AN APT NAME FOR THE FUTURE RULER OF GARHA.

THREE YEARS PASSED. BIR NARAYAN WAS NOW A MISCHIEVOUS INFANT.

NO FAMILY MUST BE AS HAPPY AS OURS IN ALL GARHA.

BUT ALAS! THE RANI'S HAPPINESS WAS NOT TO LAST FOR LONG. DALPAT FELL SERIOUSLY ILL AND WAS BEDRIDDEN.

A FEW DAYS LATER, AS DURGAVATI WAS OUT IN THE GARDEN WITH BIR NARAYAN—

RANI! RANI! THE PRINCE...

DALPAT WAS NO MORE. YOUNG DURGAVATI WAS WIDOWED. AS A RAJPUTNI*, HER FIRST THOUGHT WAS TO JOIN HER HUSBAND IN DEATH. BUT —

NO! FOR THE SAKE OF MY SON I MUST NOT GIVE IN TO MY GRIEF. GREAT TASKS LIE AHEAD OF ME.

I MUST PROVE WORTHY OF MY NOBLE ANCESTRY AND RULE THE KINGDOM WITH COURAGE TILL YOU COME OF AGE.

* RAJPUT WOMAN

RANI DURGAVATI SOON ENDEARED HERSELF TO THE PEOPLE.

THE RANI IS LIKE A MOTHER TO US.

YES SHE WILL NOT PERMIT EVEN THE LOWLIEST TO BE UNHAPPY FOR A MOMENT.

THAT'S TRUE. THERE IS NONE TO EQUAL HER IN JUSTICE.

ONE DAY —

RANI! RANI! BAZ BAHADUR* IS HERE AGAIN.

DON'T WORRY. WE'LL SEND HIM BACK.

THE UNDAUNTED RANI INSTILLED CONFIDENCE IN HER SOLDIERS.

WE HAVE 20,000 GOOD CAVALRY AND A THOUSAND ELEPHANTS. GET READY FOR BATTLE.

* A NEIGHBOURING AFGHAN RULER

THE BATTLE WAS A FIERCE ONE. BUT THE RANI AND HER TROOPS EMERGED VICTORIOUS.

BAZ BAHADUR DID NOT GIVE UP. HE MADE SEVERAL SUBSEQUENT ATTEMPTS. BUT IN EVERY ENCOUNTER THE RANI SENT HIM BACK WITH A DEPLETED ARMY.

AFTER SEVERAL SUCH ATTACKS, HOWEVER—

OUR COFFERS ARE EMPTY. THE WARS WITH BAZ BAHADUR AND HIS MEN HAVE COST US A GREAT DEAL.

WHEN THE RANI REMAINED SILENT, DEEP IN THOUGHT —

I SUGGEST WE INCREASE THE TAXES ON OUR PEOPLE.

NO! MONEY LOST IN WAR SHALL BE WON BY WAR.

RALLY OUR MEN. WE SHALL ATTACK THE PETTY RAJAS OF THE LAND.

RAJA AFTER RAJA WAS ATTACKED.

AND EACH TIME THE RANI AND HER SOLDIERS WERE THE VICTORS.

CARRY AWAY ALL THE TREASURE YOU CAN FIND. BUT LEAVE THE CITY INTACT.

SOON, THE ONCE EMPTY COFFERS WERE OVERFLOWING WITH WEALTH.

WE CAN NOW TURN OUR ATTENTION TO CIVIL MATTERS AND THE WELFARE OF THE PEOPLE.

THE PEOPLE OF GARHA THRIVED UNDER HER PROTECTION.

IF IT WERE NOT FOR OUR RANI, GARHA WOULD LONG HAVE FALLEN INTO ALIEN HANDS!

YES! THE DAY OUR PRINCE DECIDED TO WIN HER HAND WAS THE HAPPIEST ONE FOR US.

AND SO THE YEARS PASSED. BIR NARAYAN WAS NOW A STRAPPING YOUNG LAD. DURGAVATI PERSONALLY SUPERVISED HIS TRAINING AND WAS PROUD OF HIS EXCELLENT PROGRESS.

THE FUTURE RULER OF GARHA IS NOT A BAD SHOT.

THE RANI WAS IMPATIENT FOR THE DAY WHEN SHE COULD PLACE BIR NARAYAN ON THE THRONE. MEANWHILE, SHE CONTINUED SERVING HER PEOPLE WITH AFFECTION AND CONCERN. ONE DAY —

RANI! RANI! A MAN-EATER WAS SEEN IN OUR VILLAGE LAST NIGHT.

WHERE?

THE RANI WAS FOND OF HUNTING AND LIKE DALPAT HER FAVOURITE GAME WAS THE TIGER.

I WILL NOT TOUCH A DROP OF WATER TILL I'VE SHOT HIM. LEAD ME TO YOUR VILLAGE.

WE WILL HAVE TO LIE IN WAIT FOR HIM AFTER DUSK.

THE RANI MOUNTED HER HORSE AND RODE BEHIND THE VILLAGER.

THEY REACHED THE VILLAGE JUST BEFORE SUNSET. AT DUSK—

LET US WAIT HERE, RANI. IT WILL SOON BE DARK. HE SHOULD COME ANY MOMENT.

SUDDENLY —

YOU CLIMB THAT TREE AND WAIT. I'LL FINISH HIM OFF.

SHE RAISED HER BOW AND TOOK AIM.

THE TIGER, SENSING DANGER, CHARGED TOWARDS THE DISTURBING SCENT.

THE RANI NEATLY AVOIDED HIM ...

...DROPPED HER BOW AND ARROW...

...AND RAISED HER GUN.

BEFORE THE TIGER COULD REALISE WHAT WAS HAPPENING, HE WAS SHOT DEAD.

THE VILLAGER CLAMBERED DOWN THE TREE AND RAN UP TO THE TIGER.

HAVE THE CARCASS CARRIED AWAY AND SEND THE SKIN TO ME.

AND THE RANI RODE BACK TO THE PALACE.

MEANWHILE, THE PROSPEROUS PROVINCE OF GARHA SOON BECAME FAMOUS AND ATTRACTED THE ATTENTION OF THE GREAT MUGHAL EMPEROR, AKBAR.

WHY HAVEN'T WE CONQUERED AND ANNEXED THIS PROVINCE BEFORE? IT NEEDS OUR PATRONAGE AND PROTECTION.

ALAMPANAH*, FROM THE EARLIEST TIMES NO MONARCH HAS BEEN ABLE TO TAKE POSSESSION OF THAT PROVINCE. AND...

...AND NOW WITH RANI DURGAVATI AS ITS RULER IT WILL BE IMPOSSIBLE!

AKBAR LOOKED SCORNFULLY AT HIM.

WHAT! GARHA RULED BY A MERE WOMAN? AND YOU SAY IT IS IMPOSSIBLE TO ANNEX IT. SEND FOR ASAF KHAN.

* REFUGE OF THE WORLD

ASAF KHAN, THE GOVERNOR OF KARA AND THE EASTERN PROVINCES, ADJOINING GARHA, PRESENTED HIMSELF BEFORE THE EMPEROR.

INVADE GARHA AND BEND ITS RANI INTO SUBMISSION!

IT SHALL BE DONE WITH EASE, ALAMPANAH.

ASAF KHAN, AT THE HEAD OF A HUGE ARMY, MARCHED UP TO GARHA.

A FRIGHTENED SOLDIER BROUGHT THE NEWS TO THE RANI.

RANI! THE MUGHALS, HEADED BY ASAF KHAN, ARE ADVANCING TOWARDS GARHA. WE ARE LOST.

THE RANI WAS UNDAUNTED.

BRING ME MY ARMOUR. GET MY ELEPHANT READY. ASK BIR NARAYAN TOO, TO PREPARE FOR BATTLE. I SHALL LEAD MY MEN AGAINST THE IMPERIAL ARMY.

ONE OF HER ADVISERS TRIED TO COUNSEL CAUTION.

OUR TROOPS ARE DISPERSED. WE HAVE NO TIME TO RALLY THEM. WOULDN'T IT BE WISER TO NEGOTIATE WITH ASAF KHAN?

NEVER! IF AKBAR WERE HERE IN PERSON I MIGHT HAVE CONSIDERED IT. NOW? NEVER!

HOW MANY MEN DO WE HAVE HERE?

A FEW HUNDREDS.

GOOD! I'LL LEAD THEM, MARCH AHEAD AND HOLD BACK THE IMPERIAL ARMY TILL YOU RALLY OUR TROOPS.

AND WITHOUT WASTING ANOTHER MOMENT, THE RANI MARCHED OUT WITH HER BRAVE SOLDIERS TO MEET ASAF KHAN AND HIS VAST ARMIES.

AN HOUR LATER—

THAT NARROW GORGE WOULD BE THE IDEAL PLACE FOR US TO STOP THEM.

THE RANI AND HER MEN CROSSED THE RIVER WHICH WAS ALMOST DRY...

...AND SET UP CAMP ON THE OPPOSITE BANK.

AFTER THEY WERE REFRESHED THEY RODE THROUGH THE GORGE TO THE OTHER END.

AFTER THIS SPOT THE GORGE GETS WIDER AND WILL NOT SERVE OUR PURPOSE. TAKE UP YOUR POSITIONS ON THE HILLS ON EITHER SIDE. I WILL REMAIN HERE WITH A FEW MEN.

MEANWHILE, LEARNING OF HER MOVEMENTS ASAF KHAN AND HIS ARMY ADVANCED TOWARDS THE GORGE.

OUR SPIES SAY THAT THE RANI HAS HARDLY A HANDFUL OF MEN.

YET, I WOULD NOT UNDER-ESTIMATE HER.

FROM THE GORGE, THE RANI AND HER MEN WATCHED ASAF KHAN APPROACH.

IMPOSING INDEED IS THE IMPERIAL ARMY! I HOPE MY MEN DON'T LOSE HEART.

THE TWO ARMIES MET.

CHARGE! ATTACK! DON'T LET THE SCOUNDRELS DEFILE OUR SOIL.

THE RANI AND HER MEN FOUGHT WITH A FURY THAT ASAF KHAN AND HIS VAST ARMY FOUND DIFFICULT TO MATCH.

HAVE I UNDERESTIMATED THE RANI?

BY EVENING, ASAF KHAN'S ARMY WAS TOTALLY ROUTED.

WE HAVE LOST FAR TOO MANY MEN. LET US RETURN TO CAMP.

PURSUE THE FUGITIVES. CHASE THEM OUT OF OUR SACRED SOIL.

WHEN THE LAST OF THE MUGHALS WAS CHASED AWAY —

WE MUST EITHER RETURN TO CAMP AND MAKE A SURPRISE ATTACK AT NIGHT OR REMAIN HERE TILL DAYBREAK TO RENEW THE BATTLE.

I DON'T THINK THEY WILL RETURN TO FIGHT. OUR MEN ARE TIRED. LET US GO BACK TO CAMP AND REST TONIGHT.

IF WE DO, ASAF KHAN WILL SCALE THE HILLS BY MORNING AND POST HIS ARTILLERY ON THEM.

I THINK THE RANI IS RIGHT.

ASAF KHAN WILL NOT RETURN.

THE OLD COUNSELLOR INSISTED AND HIS WORD PREVAILED.

THE NEXT MORNING, WHAT THE RANI HAD PREDICTED HAPPENED. TO MAKE MATTERS WORSE, THE SKIES WERE DARK AND THE CLOUDS THREATENED TO BURST ANY MOMENT.

COURAGE, MY MEN. WE WILL NOT GIVE UP. LET US ATTACK. I WILL LEAD YOU.

AS THE RANI, MOUNTED ON HER BEST ELEPHANT, LED THE CHARGE, THE RAIN CAME DOWN IN TORRENTS.

BIR NARAYAN WAS AMONG THE FIRST TO BE WOUNDED.

TAKE HIM AWAY TO SAFETY.

MANY OF THE SOLDIERS, WHO WERE LOSING HEART, TOOK ADVANTAGE OF THE SITUATION.

LET US GO WITH HIM AND SAVE OUR LIVES TOO, WHILE WE CAN.

YES. THE RANI IS RECKLESS. SHE SHOULD NEGOTIATE.

THE RANI, HOWEVER, FOUGHT ON. AN ARROW PIERCED HER TEMPLE BUT SHE PULLED IT OUT AND ...

... CONTINUED FIGHTING.

ANOTHER ARROW PIERCED HER NECK. SHE COULD HARDLY SIT ON HER ELEPHANT.

WHATEVER COURAGE MY MEN HAVE, WILL VANISH WHEN THEY SEE ME WOUNDED. IT WOULD BE WISER NOW TO RETREAT AND FIGHT FROM MY FORTRESS.

BUT THE RANI WAS NOT FATED TO WORK OUT HER PLAN. WHEN SHE REACHED THE RIVER BANK —

WE CANNOT GO ACROSS. THE RIVER HAS RISEN AND IS UNFORDABLE.

THE RANI HAD TO THINK FAST. THE ENEMY WAS CLOSING IN UPON HER.

RANI, PLEASE LET ME TAKE YOU TO A SAFE PLACE.

THE RANI SCORNED HIS SUGGESTION.

AND PERCHANCE FALL INTO THE HANDS OF THE ENEMY. NO! I AM OVERCOME IN BATTLE. GOD FORBID THAT I ALSO BE OVERCOME IN NAME AND HONOUR.

SHE PULLED OUT HER DAGGER.

I WOULD RATHER DIE IN HONOUR THAN LIVE IN DISGRACE.

AND LIKE THE TRUE RAJPUTNI THAT SHE WAS, THE PROUD RANI STABBED HERSELF.